"Introduction to Optical Components”

SIMONE MALACRIDA

The following topics are presented in this book:
dielectric waveguides, flat plate and guided propagation
acousto-optic and electro-optic modulators
optical amplifiers
optical gratings
lasers

Simone Malacrida (1977)
Engineer and writer, has worked on research, finance, energy policy and industrial plants.

AUTHOR'S NOTE:
This book addresses topics of a physical-engineering nature for the understanding of which it is essential to know the prerequisites of mathematical analysis and advanced physics.

ANALYTICAL INDEX

INTRODUCTION

In this book, the main optical components that translate the majority of the interaction effects between electromagnetic waves and matter into technological practice are presented in a summary way.
The importance of these components has grown in recent decades in relation to the extraordinary development of telecommunications and, in general, of the entire information technology sector.
On the other hand, basic physics had already highlighted the main characteristics of lasers and optical components since the 1960s, perfecting the physics of matter, solid state and semiconductors.
As such, this book certainly does not claim to be exhaustive or to cover notions that range between different technological university courses.
Rather, the intent is to focus on the physical mechanisms and underlying equations of those components.
For this reason, the contents of this manual are suitable for those who already have an understanding of mathematics, physics and technology at the university level.

THE

THE GUIDES AND THE FLAT SLAB

Introduction

A dielectric waveguide is a component in which a given electromagnetic wave is able to propagate in a particular direction while remaining confined in a limited portion of the plane, transverse to the same direction of propagation.
This is the concept of **guided propagation** , the basis of all optical and electro-optical components.
The physical mechanisms underlying this propagation reside in the particularity of some materials, called dielectrics, for which there is a different electrical permittivity in the various directions and, at the same time, there is a phenomenon of total reflection.
Under these conditions, Maxwell's equations governing the electromagnetic wave manage to define self-sustaining functions, the so-called **modes** .

The ways

We consider a cylindrical structure in the z direction.
Maxwell's equations can be expressed as:

$$\overline{e}(u_1, u_2, z) = \overline{E}(u_1, u_2)e^{-\gamma z}$$

$$\overline{h}(u_1, u_2, z) = \overline{H}(u_1, u_2)e^{-\gamma z},$$

Gamma is called **the propagation constant** and can be expressed as follows:

$$\gamma = \alpha + j\beta$$

In turn, alpha is called **attenuation constant** and beta **phase constant** , as they act respectively on the amplitude of the wave and on its phase.
The functions E and H which describe the electric and magnetic fields in the direction transverse to the direction of propagation, are called **modes** .
From Maxwell's equations it follows that:

$$\overline{E}_t(u_1, u_2) = \frac{j}{\omega^2\mu\varepsilon - \beta^2}\left(- \beta\overline{\nabla}_t E_z - \omega\mu\overline{\nabla}_t H_z \times \hat{z}\right);$$

$$\overline{H}_t(u_1, u_2) = \frac{j}{\omega^2\mu\varepsilon - \beta^2}\left(- \beta\overline{\nabla}_t H_z + \omega\mu\overline{\nabla}_t E_z \times \hat{z}\right).$$

Where the material is homogeneous, these equations fall into Helmholtz's more general formulation:

$$\nabla_t^2 \phi + (\omega^2 \mu \varepsilon - \beta^2)\phi = 0,$$

A generic mode carries such a **power** :

$$P = \int_S \frac{1}{2}\left(\overline{e} \times \overline{h}^*\right) \cdot \hat{z}\, dS = \int_S \frac{1}{2} |A|^2 e^{-2\alpha z} \left(\overline{E} \times \overline{H}^*\right) \cdot \hat{z}\, dS = |A|^2 e^{-2\alpha z}.$$

From which we can deduce the name given to the alpha constant.
It can be shown that the modes represent a basis of solutions for cylindrical structures ie they are complete, orthogonal and orthonormal.

Transfer function

Given a dielectric waveguide of length L, if we measure the field at the exit and at the entrance of the same and we calculate the ratio, we obtain the **transfer function of the guide** :

$$F(\omega) = e^{-\alpha(\omega)L} e^{-j\beta(\omega)L}$$

We define **equiphase surfaces** of the planes orthogonal to the direction of invariance of the cylindrical structure.

These surfaces propagate at the following **phase velocity** :

$$v_f = \frac{\omega_0}{\beta}.$$

It can be seen that the time it takes for a surface to cover the guide is given by:

$$\tau_f = \frac{L}{v_f} = \frac{\beta L}{\omega_0}.$$

This time is called **phase delay** .

Types of guides

Waveguides are distinguished by their geometry.
There are rectangular guides integrated in a more or less superficial way in other materials or widespread guides, i.e. with non-rectangular but curvilinear geometry.
There is particular interest for curved guides, in fact the phase speed is no longer a constant but depends on the radius of curvature of the guide and the position considered:

$$v_f(r) = v_{fR}\frac{r}{R},$$

$$v_{fR} = \frac{\omega}{\beta}$$

There is therefore a critical radius of curvature given by:

$$v_f(r_c) = \frac{c}{n_{cl}}.$$

Where the denominator is the refractive index of the material in which the guide is immersed.
Beyond this radius, the speed required at the equiphase surfaces is excessive and there is a net loss of wave mode.
The critical radius is:

$$r_c = R\frac{\beta}{2\pi n_{cl}}.$$

The greater the radius of curvature of the waveguide, the less there will be losses in the curved guides.

Applications

A first application of waveguides is that of the **directional coupler** , i.e. a way of making an electromagnetic wave propagate in two parallel but different structures.
Having two different structures, the modes of one and the other will interfere as happens for any electromagnetic wave.
The resulting modes will be given by the sum (even modes) or the difference (odd modes) of the respective initial modes.
A fundamental condition is that these modes do not degenerate in phase, i.e. it must exist that:

$$\beta_d - \beta_p = \Delta\beta \neq 0.$$

Having defined the two refractive indices, we can find the length for which the two modes are in phase opposition.
This value is called **the coupling length** :

$$L_c = \frac{\pi}{\Delta\beta} = \frac{\pi}{\Delta n_{eff}} \frac{\lambda}{2\pi} = \frac{\lambda}{2\Delta n_{eff}},$$

A further application of waveguides is the **polarization converter** .

With this device, the polarization of an electromagnetic wave can be changed simply by introducing a waveguide which causes a delay in the phase constant.
For example, to rotate the polarization by 90°, a waveguide of this length must be interposed:

$$L = \frac{\lambda}{2(n_{eff1} - n_{eff2})};$$

Having indicated the effective refractive indices of the first and second modes.

The flat slab

We dedicate a separate paragraph to the flat plate which constitutes the simplest dielectric waveguide.
By flat plate we mean a three-dimensional area confined in one direction only within a defined thickness.
Inside the slab there will be a given refractive index, outside there will be a different one (obviously this is due to the difference in material between the internal part, called core and the external one, called cladding).
We assume the propagation constant purely imaginary, i.e. without any attenuation phenomenon.
Consider a structure confined along the y axis, the electric and magnetic fields in the other directions will be:

I – The guides and the flat slab

$$E_x = -j\frac{\beta}{\tilde{k}_x^2}\frac{dE_z}{dx}$$

$$E_y = j\eta_0\frac{k_0}{\tilde{k}_x^2}\frac{dH_z}{dx}$$

$$H_x = -j\frac{\beta}{\tilde{k}_x^2}\frac{dH_z}{dx}$$

$$H_y = j\frac{n^2}{\eta_0}\frac{k_0}{\tilde{k}_x^2}\frac{dE_z}{dx}$$

Where is valid:

$$\tilde{k}_x = \sqrt{\omega^2\mu\varepsilon - \beta^2} = \sqrt{n^2k_0^2 - \beta^2}.$$

Since the medium is homogeneous, the Helmoltz equation must hold:

$$\frac{d^2\phi}{dx^2} + \tilde{k}_x^2\phi = 0$$

Whose general solutions are:

I – The guides and the flat slab

$$\phi(x) = \tilde{A}e^{-j\tilde{k}_x x} + \tilde{B}e^{j\tilde{k}_x x}.$$

We note that the guided modes in the flat plate only exist for these beta values:

$$n_{cl}k_0 < \beta < n_{co}k_0$$

Conversely, for other values there are radiating modes or zones forbidden by the same Maxwell equations.
We note that, rewriting the relation as follows:

$$k_x^2 + \gamma^2 = k_0^2(n_{co}^2 - n_{cl}^2).$$

The solutions are as follows (the first is valid in the part above the flat slab, the last in the one below, while the central value corresponds to the wave inside the flat slab):

$$\phi(x) = \begin{cases} b_1 e^{-\gamma x} + b_3 e^{\gamma x} \\ a_1 \sin(k_x.x) + a_2 \cos(k_x.x) \\ b_2 e^{\gamma x} + b_4 e^{-\gamma x} \end{cases}$$

Imposing that the solution does not diverge to infinity, we have:

$$b_3 = b_4 = 0.$$

Now, there are two types of modes depending on whether the transverse electric field or the magnetic field is zero. For TE modes, it will be:

$$H_z(x) = \begin{cases} b_1 e^{-\gamma z} \\ a_1 \sin(k_x x) + a_2 \cos(k_x x) \\ b_2 e^{\gamma z} \end{cases}$$

$$E_y(x) = \begin{cases} j\eta_0 \frac{k_0}{\gamma} b_1 e^{-\gamma z} \\ j\eta_0 \frac{k_0}{k_x} (a_1 \cos(k_x x) + a_2 \sin(k_x x)) \\ -j\eta_0 \frac{k_0}{\gamma} b_2 e^{\gamma z} \end{cases}$$

$$H_x = -\frac{\beta}{\eta_0 k_0} E_y.$$

$$E_z = 0$$

While, for TM modes:

$$H_z = 0$$

$$E_z(x) = \begin{cases} b_1 e^{-\gamma z} \\ a_1 \sin(k_x x) + a_2 \cos(k_x x) \\ b_2 e^{\gamma z} \end{cases}$$

$$H_y(x) = \begin{cases} -j\frac{n_{cl}^2}{\eta_0}\frac{k_0}{\gamma}b_1 e^{-\gamma z} \\ -j\frac{n_{co}^2}{\eta_0}\frac{k_0}{k_x}(a_1\cos(k_x x) + a_2\sin(k_x x)) \\ j\frac{n_{cl}^2}{\eta_0}\frac{k_0}{\gamma}b_2 e^{\gamma z} \end{cases}$$

$$E_x = \begin{cases} \frac{\beta\eta_0}{n_{co}^2 k_0}H_y \\ \frac{\beta\eta_0}{n_{cl}^2 k_0}H_y \end{cases}$$

We note that both modes can in turn be divided into even and odd based on the symmetry of the trigonometric function which defines the trend in the core.
Introducing these normalized quantities:

$$\begin{aligned} u &= k_x d; \\ w &= \gamma d; \\ v &= k_0 d\sqrt{n_{co}^2 - n_{cl}^2}. \end{aligned}$$

It is found that the equations for modes TE (even and odd) and TM (even and odd), are:

$$
\begin{aligned}
w &= u\tan(u) \\
w &= -u\cot(u) \\
w &= \frac{n_{cl}^2}{n_{cl}^2}u\tan(u) \\
w &= -\frac{n_{cl}^2}{n_{cl}^2}u\cot(u)
\end{aligned}
$$

For each mode, we can therefore define a wavelength (called cut-off) such that there is no longer any other higher order mode.
In particular, if:

$$\lambda > 2d\sqrt{n_{co}^2 - n_{cl}^2}.$$

Then there will be only one guided way in the flatbed.

II

THE MODULATORS

Introduction

Modulators play an essential role in optical communications and in general in the transformation of electromagnetic waves.
Their task is precisely that of modulating an electromagnetic source.
As everyone knows from the rudiments of electrical communications, there are several types of modulation.
Typically, wave amplitudes or frequencies can be modulated.
The modulators that we will present in this chapter manage to transform the information present in on-wave communications on the basis of some physical principles typical of certain materials.
By exploiting these principles, a modulation of the wave is induced.
A first question could arise about the very nature of modulation.
How come you don't try a road similar to that of radio waves by directly modulating the source?
The answer to that question is soon revealed.

In optical communications, the sources of information are almost always lasers.
However, the direct modulation of a laser source is a very inefficient physical process.
Here, therefore, that the modulators become essential and must be studied as components in their own right.

Physical principles

There are many physical principles underlying the functioning of modulators.
The Franz-Keldysh effect is an electro-optical effect which occurs in silicon: by applying an external electric field, a variation of the edge of the energy bands is observed.
There is therefore a variation of both the absorption spectrum and the refractive index.
This effect is therefore combined by an electro-absorption effect **and** an **electro -refraction effect** .
Returning to the propagation constant, already presented in the first chapter, we have:

$$\gamma = \alpha + j\beta$$

Where alpha and beta can be expressed like this:

$$\begin{cases} \alpha = \dfrac{k}{\sqrt{2}}\sqrt{\sqrt{1+R^2}-1}; \\ \\ \beta = \dfrac{k}{\sqrt{2}}\sqrt{\sqrt{1+R^2}+1}; \end{cases}$$

$$k = \omega\sqrt{\mu\varepsilon}$$
$$R = \sigma/\omega\varepsilon$$

The typical quantities of the propagation are therefore related to the physical characteristics of the material, in particular with the conductivity and the dielectric permittivity.
Striking a semiconductor material with an optical beam of a given pulse, the polarization vector is given by:

$$P = -\frac{q^2E}{\omega^2}\left[\frac{N_e}{m_e^*}\left(1-\frac{j\gamma_e}{\omega}\right)+\frac{N_h}{m_h^*}\left(1-\frac{j\gamma_h}{\omega}\right)\right],$$

Recalling the relationship between polarization and susceptibility:

$$P = \varepsilon_o(n^2-1)E = \varepsilon_o\chi E,$$

We can find the real and imaginary parts of this quantity:

$$\begin{cases} \chi_r = -\dfrac{q^2}{\varepsilon_r \omega^3}\left(\dfrac{N_e}{m_e^*} + \dfrac{N_h}{m_h^*}\right); \\ \chi_i = \dfrac{q^2}{\varepsilon_r \omega^3}\left(\dfrac{N_e \gamma_e}{m_e^*} + \dfrac{N_h \gamma_h}{m_h^*}\right); \end{cases}$$

Finally, recalling the link between susceptibility, refractive index and absorption coefficient, we can obtain the values of the latter and their variations:

$$\begin{cases} n = n_0\left[1 - \dfrac{q^2}{2\varepsilon \omega^3}\left(\dfrac{N_e}{m_e^*} + \dfrac{N_h}{m_h^*}\right)\right] \\ \alpha = \dfrac{\pi n_0 q^2}{\lambda \varepsilon \omega^3}\left(\dfrac{N_e \gamma_e}{m_e^*} + \dfrac{N_h \gamma_h}{m_h^*}\right) \end{cases}$$

$$\begin{cases} \Delta n = -\dfrac{q^2 \lambda^2}{8\pi^2 c^2 \varepsilon_0 n}\left(\dfrac{\Delta N_e}{m_e^*} + \dfrac{\Delta N_h}{m_h^*}\right) \\ \Delta \alpha = \dfrac{q^3 \lambda^2}{4\pi^2 c^3 \varepsilon_0 n}\left(\dfrac{\Delta N_e}{m_e^{*2} \mu_e} + \dfrac{\Delta N_h}{m_h^{*2} \mu_h}\right) \end{cases}$$

These values depend on universal constants, on material constants (the mobility of electrons and holes, the effective mass of electrons and holes) and on the concentration of electrons and holes inside the semiconductor.

To obtain modulated signals it is therefore sufficient to vary the concentration of carriers inside the semiconductor.
Based on the way in which this concentration varies, the various types of modulator can be classified.

Acousto-optic modulators

The acousto-optic modulators exploit the physical principle of the acousto-optic effect according to which there is an interference between acoustic waves and electromagnetic waves inside some materials.
Consider a plane acoustic wave:

$$s(x,t) = S_0 \cos(\Omega t - qx).$$

Due to the acousto-optic effect there is a variation of the refractive index of the material:

$$\Delta n(x,t) = -\frac{1}{2} p n^3 s(x,t),$$

Where p is a suitable photoelastic constant.
It will mean that the refractive index will be characterized by a periodic trend that reflects the trend of the acoustic wave:

$$n(x,t) = n - \Delta n_0 \cos(\Omega t - qx),$$

The magnitude of this variation is given by:

$$\Delta n_0 = \frac{1}{2} p n^3 S_0.$$

By defining the intensity of the acoustic wave as:

$$I_s = \frac{1}{2} \varrho v_s^3 S_0^2,$$

We can rewrite the amplitude like this:

$$\Delta n_0 = \left(\frac{1}{2} M I_s\right)^{1/2},$$

Where this constant:

$$\mathcal{M} = \frac{p^2 n^6}{\varrho v_s^3},$$

It is a characteristic parameter of the medium and constitutes a figure of merit for the acousto-optic effect in a given material.

A plane optical wave that maintains a constant intensity as it passes through the acousto-optic modulator will have a total reflectivity of:

$$R = \frac{1}{2} j r' d \; sinc \left[(q - 2k \sin\theta) \frac{d}{2\pi} \right] e^{j\Omega t},$$

Where d is the thickness of the modulator, k is the modulus of the wave vector and r' is given by the following quantity:

$$r' = \frac{-q}{2n \sin^2\theta} \Delta n_0.$$

The reflectivity maximum will occur when the argument in square brackets is null, i.e. when:

$$\sin\theta_B = \frac{\lambda}{2\Lambda},$$

This condition is called Bragg's and the angle for which this happens is called Bragg's.

Electro-optical modulators

The electro-optical modulators have higher performances than previously exposed.
The physical principle underlying these modulators is **the electro-optical effect** .
By applying an electric field, there are variations in the optical properties of the medium.
Typically, this is reflected in a change in the refractive index of the material.
Let us consider the dielectric impermeability tensor:

$$\hat{\eta} = \begin{pmatrix} \eta_{xx} & \eta_{xy} & \eta_{xz} \\ \eta_{yx} & \eta_{yy} & \eta_{yz} \\ \eta_{zx} & \eta_{zy} & \eta_{zz} \end{pmatrix} = \varepsilon_0 \begin{pmatrix} \varepsilon_{xx}^{-1} & \varepsilon_{xy}^{-1} & \varepsilon_{xz}^{-1} \\ \varepsilon_{yx}^{-1} & \varepsilon_{yy}^{-1} & \varepsilon_{yz}^{-1} \\ \varepsilon_{zx}^{-1} & \varepsilon_{zy}^{-1} & \varepsilon_{zz}^{-1} \end{pmatrix}$$

Considering a passive and lossless medium we have:

$$\hat{\eta} = \begin{pmatrix} \frac{1}{n_x^2} & 0 & 0 \\ 0 & \frac{1}{n_y^2} & 0 \\ 0 & 0 & \frac{1}{n_z^2} \end{pmatrix},$$

This tensor can be translated into the following relation that binds the refractive indices, the so-called ellipsoid of the indices:

$$\frac{x^2}{n_x^2} + \frac{y^2}{n_y^2} + \frac{z^2}{n_z^2} = 1.$$

By applying an electric field, a change of the following type is induced:

$$\eta_{ij}(E) - \eta_{ij}(0) = \Delta\eta_{ij} = \sum_{k=1}^{3}\left(r_{ijk}E_k + \sum_{l=1}^{3} s_{ijkl}E_kE_l\right)$$

Where the coefficients are defined as follows:

$$\begin{cases} r_{ijk} = \left[\dfrac{\partial\eta_{ij}}{\partial E_k}\right]_{\bar{\mathbf{E}}=0}; \\ \\ s_{ijkl} = \left[\dfrac{1}{2}\dfrac{\partial^2\eta_{ij}}{\partial E_k \partial E_l}\right]_{\bar{\mathbf{E}}=0}. \end{cases}$$

The first coefficients are called linear electro-optical coefficients (or Pockels), the second ones are quadratic (or Kerr).
Depending on their presence, therefore, there are different electro-optical effects.

For **the Pockels effect** , considering a non-active and lossless medium, the ellipsoid of the indices is given by:

$$x^2\left(\frac{1}{n_x^2}+\Delta_1\right)+y^2\left(\frac{1}{n_y^2}+\Delta_2\right)+z^2\left(\frac{1}{n_z^2}+\Delta_3\right)+2yz\Delta_4+2xz\Delta_5+2xy\Delta_6=1.$$

The most common material for electro-optical modulators is lithium niobate.
In this medium, the index ellipsoid becomes:

$$x^2\left(\frac{1}{n_o^2}+r_{13}E\right)+y^2\left(\frac{1}{n_o^2}+r_{13}E\right)+z^2\left(\frac{1}{n_e^2}+r_{33}E\right)=1.$$

From which it can be deduced that:

$$\begin{cases} n_x \simeq n_o - \frac{1}{2}n_o^3 r_{13}E; \\ n_y \simeq n_o - \frac{1}{2}n_o^3 r_{13}E; \\ n_z \simeq n_e - \frac{1}{2}n_e^3 r_{33}E. \end{cases}$$

These are the new refractive indices along the axes of the crystal.
We can define **birefringence** as:

$$n_z - n_y = (n_e - n_o) - \frac{1}{2}(n_e^3 r_{33} - n_o^3 r_{13})E.$$

A lithium niobate modulator in integrated optics of the Mach-Zehnder type (i.e. with two distinct branches of the interferometer), has an output intensity given by:

$$I_o = I_i cos^2 \frac{\Delta\phi}{2},$$

Where the phase difference is expressed as follows:

$$\Delta\phi = (\beta_2 - \beta_1)L$$

And it crucially depends on the length of the modulator.
We note that the task of the modulator is precisely that of creating a periodic variation of some physical parameters of the incoming wave.
Based on the physical quantities of the modulator we can therefore choose whether to have a total (destructive interference) or partial modulation mechanism.

II – Modulators

III

OPTICAL AMPLIFIERS

Introduction

Optical amplifiers play a primary role in purely optical transmissions.
Although light signals can travel for hundreds of kilometers in optical fiber without undergoing significant attenuation (this only happens at certain wavelengths), there is still a need to amplify the signal over very long distances (such as transoceanic ones).
Let us immediately point out that optical amplification is completely different on a physical and technological level from electrical amplification.
In fact, in the latter, the signal must be somehow regenerated and remodulated, as well as being amplified.
Optical amplifiers, on the other hand, act only on the power of the signal, expanding it, without changing its shape in the least.
There are two large families of optical amplifiers, the semiconductor ones and the fiber optic one.

Physical principles

The interaction between electromagnetic waves and matter can take place according to the three mechanisms shown below.

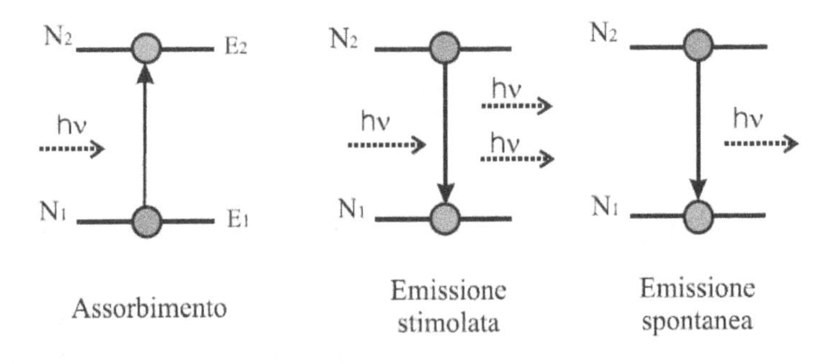

Absorption is the physical phenomenon whereby an incident photon is captured and creates an electron-hole pair in the conduction and valence bands.
Spontaneous emission instead considers the opposite process, ie when a spontaneous recombination between electrons and holes generates an emission of photons.
The stimulated emission instead exploits an incident wave for the emission of a further photon at the same frequency.
Optical amplifiers, like lasers, mainly exploit this physical principle.
We define the absorption frequency as the following quantity:

$$W_{12} = \sigma_{12}\frac{I}{h\nu}.$$

Where an absorption cross section appears.
The population change in the fundamental level is given by:

$$\frac{dN_1}{dt} = -W_{12}N_1 = -\sigma_{12}\frac{I}{h\nu}N_1.$$

On the other hand, we define an emission frequency as follows:

$$W_{21} = \sigma_{21}\frac{I}{h\nu}$$

The population change of the stimulated level is given by:

$$\frac{dN_2}{dt} = -W_{21}N_2 = -\sigma_{21}\frac{I}{h\nu}N_2$$

For spontaneous emission, its probability is inversely proportional to the lifetime:

$$A_{21} = \frac{1}{\tau}.$$

The contribution of this emission to the population change of the stimulated level is as follows:

$$\frac{dN_2}{dt} = -A_{21}\,N_2 = -\frac{N_2}{\tau}$$

Typology

The gain of an optical amplifier measures the ratio of output power to input power.
The gain band is the frequency range in which the amplifier is effective.
The gain saturation point is that power value for which the output power does not increase despite an increase in input power.
Polarization sensitivity refers to the dependence of gain on signal polarization.
The noise of an optical amplifier is given almost exclusively by the spontaneous emission mechanism.

A semiconductor optical amplifier is a semiconductor laser in which a mechanism similar to that of a Fabry-Perot cavity takes place.
By exploiting the mechanism of multiple reflections (with constructive interference) it is possible to amplify the input laser source by a given gain factor.
For this reason, the study of these amplifiers is very similar to that of semiconductor lasers.

Much more interesting from a theoretical and practical point of view is the case of fiber optic amplifiers.
Quite simply, a fiber optical amplifier is a suitably doped optical fiber.
In terms of communications, optical fibers doped with rare earths are particularly interesting.
Depending on the type of rare earths, it is possible to cover different frequency bands.
Among all, the most common optical amplifier is the one with erbium doping, as this rare earth allows to exploit the band in which the optical fibers have the lowest possible attenuation.
We can write the variation of the population of the stimulated level in an amplifier of this type as follows:

$$\frac{dN_2}{dt} = \sum_{k=1}^{N} N_1(r,\phi,z)\sigma_{ak}\frac{I_k}{h\nu_k} - \sum_{k=1}^{N} N_2(r,\phi,z)\sigma_{ek}\frac{I_k}{h\nu_k} - \frac{N_2(r,\phi,z)}{\tau}.$$

In stationary regime, it must hold that:

$$N_2(r,\phi,z) = N_T \frac{\sum_{k=1}^{N} \tau\sigma_{ak}\frac{I_k}{h\nu_k}}{1+\sum_{k=1}^{N} \tau(\sigma_{ak}+\sigma_{ek})\frac{I_k}{h\nu_k}},$$

However, we must consider that the principle of detailed balance (another form of expressing the conservation of mass) always holds:

$$N_1(r,\phi,z) + N_2(r,\phi,z) = N_T(r,\phi,z).$$

The optical power of a beam of light is defined as follows:

$$P_k(z) = \int_0^{2\pi} \int_0^{\infty} I_k(r,\phi,z) r\, dr\, d\phi$$

The variation of this power on a stretch of doped fiber will be:

$$\begin{aligned} \frac{dP_k}{dz} = & \pm\sigma_{ek} N_2(z) P_k(z) \int_0^{2\pi} \int_0^{b} i_k(r,\phi)\, r\, dr\, d\phi + \\ & \mp\sigma_{ak} N_1(z) P_k(z) \int_0^{2\pi} \int_0^{b} i_k(r,\phi)\, r\, dr\, d\phi + \\ & \pm\sigma_{ek} N_2(z) 2h\nu_k \Delta\nu_k \int_0^{2\pi} \int_0^{b} i_k(r,\phi)\, r\, dr\, d\phi \end{aligned}$$

We define overlap integral between the mode at the considered frequency and the dopant as:

$$\Gamma_k = \int_0^{2\pi} \int_0^{b} i_k(r,\phi)\, r\, dr\, d\phi.$$

The power can therefore be rewritten:

$$\frac{dP_k}{dz} = \pm\sigma_{ek}N_2(z)P_k(z)\Gamma_k \mp \sigma_{ak}N_1(z)P_k(z)\Gamma_k \pm \sigma_{ek}N_2(z)2h\nu_k\Delta\nu_k\Gamma_k$$

We define the absorption coefficient and the gain coefficient as:

$$\begin{aligned} \alpha_k &= \Gamma_k\sigma_{ak}N_T \\ g_k &= \Gamma_k\sigma_{ek}N_T \end{aligned}$$

From which it follows that:

$$\frac{dP_k}{dz} = \pm g_k\frac{N_2(z)}{N_T}P_k(z) \mp \alpha_k\frac{N_1(z)}{N_T}P_k(z) \pm g_k\frac{N_2(z)}{N_T}2h\nu_k\Delta\nu_k\Gamma_k.$$

$$\frac{N_2}{N_T} = \frac{\sum_k \tau\alpha_k\frac{P_k}{h\nu_k\,\pi b^2 N_T}}{1+\sum_k \tau(\alpha_k+g_k)\frac{P_k}{h\nu_k\,\pi b^2 N_T}}.$$

If we have a complete population inversion, the power will be amplified precisely by the gain factor just defined:

$$P_k(z=L) = P_k(z=0)\,e^{g_k L}.$$

Conversely, if we had no population inversion, the power would be attenuated by the absorption coefficient.

Physically we will never be in one of these extreme cases, but we will have a mixed situation, where the power will depend on the gain and absorption cross sections:

$$\frac{dP_k}{dz} = \pm \left(\sigma_{ek} N_2(z) - \sigma_{ak} N_1(z)\right)\Gamma_k P_k(z).$$

The condition to have a profit will therefore be:

$$(\sigma_{ek} N_2(z) - \sigma_{ak} N_1(z)) > 0.$$

IV

THE GRATINGS

Introduction

A diffraction grating is an important optical component whose properties are based on the Bragg condition already expressed above:

$$\Lambda = \frac{\lambda}{2n},$$

$$\lambda_{Bragg} = 2n_{eff}\Lambda$$

Under this condition, the reflected waves are all in phase and constructively interfere allowing almost total reflection of a given wavelength.
The characterizing aspects of a grating are therefore the refractive index and the lambda constant known as the pitch of the grating.
Another fundamental aspect is the modulation profile of the refractive index which can be sinusoidal, rectangular

or of other shapes , thus characterizing the properties of the grating.

Physical principles

Theoretically, we always start from Maxwell's equations and the transverse nabla operator:

$$\overline{\nabla}_t = \overline{\nabla} - \frac{\partial}{\partial z}\hat{z}.$$

To arrive at the equations that determine the electric and magnetic fields under perturbation conditions:

$$\overline{E}_{Pt}(x,y,z) = \sum_{\nu} (a_\nu + b_\nu)\,\overline{E}_{t\nu}(x,y)$$

$$\overline{H}_{Pt}(x,y,z) = \sum_{\nu} (a_\nu - b_\nu)\,\overline{H}_{t\nu}(x,y).$$

Where the following coefficients refer to direct modes (i.e. in the same direction of wave propagation):

$$a_\nu(z) = A_\nu(z)\,e^{-j\beta_\nu z}$$

While these coefficients at the reflected modes:

$$b_\nu(z) = B_\nu(z)\, e^{j\beta_\nu z}$$

The following ratio is called the reflection coefficient:

$$\Gamma(z) = \frac{B(z)}{A(z)};$$

Considering only the direct modes we arrive at a coupling equation between copropagating modes, considering only the reflected modes instead we have a coupling equation between counterpropagating modes:

$$\frac{da_\mu}{dz} + j\beta_\mu a_\mu = -j\sum_\nu \left(K^+_{\nu\mu} a_\nu + K^-_{\nu\mu} b_\nu\right)$$

$$\frac{db_\mu}{dz} - j\beta_\mu b_\mu = j\sum_\nu \left(K^-_{\nu\mu} a_\nu + K^+_{\nu\mu} b_\nu\right)$$

Where is it:

$$K^+_{\nu\mu} = K^t_{\nu\mu} + K^z_{\nu\mu}$$

$$K^-_{\nu\mu} = K^t_{\nu\mu} - K^z_{\nu\mu}$$

propagating and counter-propagating coupling coefficients , while:

$$K^t_{\nu\mu} = \omega \iint\limits_{-\infty}^{+\infty} \Delta\varepsilon \overline{E}_{t\nu} \overline{E}^*_{t\mu} \, dx \, dy$$

$$K^z_{\nu\mu} = \omega \iint\limits_{-\infty}^{+\infty} \frac{\varepsilon \cdot \Delta\varepsilon}{\varepsilon + \Delta\varepsilon} \overline{E}_{z\nu} \overline{E}^*_{z\mu} \, dx \, dy.$$

They are the transversal and longitudinal coupling coefficients.
By defining, in the two propagation cases, the phase differences as:

$$\delta = \beta_\nu - \beta_\mu \pm \frac{2\pi}{\Lambda},$$
$$\delta = \beta_\nu + \beta_\mu \pm \frac{2\pi}{\Lambda}.$$

The Bragg condition (also called phase-matching condition) is satisfied for:

$$\beta_\nu - \beta_\mu \cong \pm\frac{2\pi}{\Lambda};$$

$$\beta_\nu + \beta_\mu \cong \pm\frac{2\pi}{\Lambda};$$

Generally speaking, we talk about short pitch gratings (or reflection gratings) for counterpropagating modes and long pitch gratings (or transmission gratings) for copropagating modes.

Guide gratings

In guide gratings the phase matching condition becomes the following for long pitch gratings:

$$\beta_\nu = \beta_\mu + \frac{2\pi}{\Lambda};$$

$$\beta_\nu = \beta_\mu - \frac{2\pi}{\Lambda};$$

And for those with a short wheelbase:

$$\beta_\nu = \frac{2\pi}{\Lambda} - \beta_\mu;$$

$$\beta_\nu = -\frac{2\pi}{\Lambda} - \beta_\mu.$$

Fiber lattices

In fiber optic gratings, a Bragg grating is characterized by a periodic modulation of the refractive index of the fiber core:

$$\delta n_{core}(z) = \overline{\delta n}_{core}(z)\left\{1 + \upsilon(z)\cos\left(\frac{2\pi z}{\Lambda(z)} + \varphi(z)\right)\right\}$$

Under single-mode conditions, the coupled-mode equations are:

$$\frac{dA}{dz} = -j\sigma_{aa}A - j\kappa^* B e^{2j\left(\beta - \frac{\pi}{\Lambda}\right)z - j\varphi};$$
$$\frac{dB}{dz} = j\sigma_{bb}B + j\kappa A e^{-2j\left(\beta - \frac{\pi}{\Lambda}\right)z + j\varphi};$$

The phase difference (called detuning parameter) is given by:

$$\delta = \beta - \frac{\pi}{\Lambda} = 2\pi n_{eff}\left(\frac{1}{\lambda} - \frac{1}{2n_{eff}\Lambda}\right) = 2\pi n_{eff}\left(\frac{1}{\lambda} - \frac{1}{\lambda_{Bragg}}\right)$$

From which we obtain the same Bragg condition found previously.

Property

We have already characterized the reflection coefficient of a grating, now we find other fundamental parameters.
The bandwidth of a lattice is given by:

$$B = \frac{\lambda^2}{2\pi n_{eff} L}\sqrt{(\kappa L)^2 + \pi^2}.$$

If the first term under the square root can be neglected, we note that the bandwidth is an inverse function of the lattice length.
The group delay for reflected light is given by:

$$\tau = \frac{d\phi}{d\omega} = -\frac{\lambda^2}{2\pi c}\frac{d\phi}{d\lambda}$$

While the chromatic dispersion of a lattice is as follows:

$$d = \frac{d\tau}{d\lambda} = -\frac{2\pi c}{\lambda^2}\frac{d^2\phi}{d\omega^2}$$

Applications

We have seen that, under the Bragg condition, there is an almost total reflection of the mode corresponding to a given wavelength.
This determines the main application of gratings as optical filters.
By composing various geometries it is possible to obtain addition or loss filters (add-drop) of a channel and it is possible to do it for many channels (multiplexer).
Furthermore the gratings can be used as mode couplers or dispersion compensators.
Another notable application is to "smooth out" the gain curve of an optical amplifier thus allowing for homogeneous amplification within the band.
Finally, the gratings can be used to modulate the pumping of a laser or to create sensors sensitive to elastic and mechanical oscillations.

IV – The gratings

V

THE LASERS

Introduction

Laser is an English acronym which, translated, is “light amplification by stimulated emission radiation”.
Therefore, in the name itself there are two fundamental references to physical principles.
It is an optical amplification mechanism whose main foundation lies in the mechanism of stimulated emission.
For a laser to exist, the following physical conditions must be present:

1) there must be a mechanism (called pumping) which allows a population inversion between a stimulated level and a fundamental level.
2) there must be light amplification.
3) this light must somehow be emitted outwards.

The first point about pumping can be done in several ways. There are pumping of a chemical, electrical and optical nature based on the medium considered.

Light amplification requires a material and an optical resonator.
The material determines the type of laser and the characteristics of the light emitted: frequency, power and so on.
There are different materials, from gases to liquids to solids, mainly semiconductors.
Consequently, there are lasers that emit ultraviolet, visible or infrared light, with powers ranging from very low values (portable laser pointers for example) to high values capable of cutting very thick metal plates.
The optical resonator not only guarantees that the laser light remains confined inside the active material (and therefore allows the amplification mechanism simply by passing the light a number of times such as to guarantee a consistent output flow), but also allows the exit of the same, not being totally reflective, right at the exit.
We will see that, under certain conditions, the laser light is self-sustaining, i.e. the population inversion guaranteed by the pumping and the leakage of part of the light however allow what remains in the material to continue the amplification mechanism, making sure that the flow is continuous.
For some applications, it is necessary to have a very powerful but pulsed flow and this too can be achieved under particular conditions.

Physical principles

We have already mentioned the mechanisms of spontaneous emission, stimulated emission and absorption with the related equations.
Here, we only recall how, generally in semiconductor lasers, the stimulated (and spontaneous) emission can occur according to two distinct mechanisms.
The figure shows situation a) which refers to direct gap semiconductors, and situation b) which refers to indirect gap semiconductors.

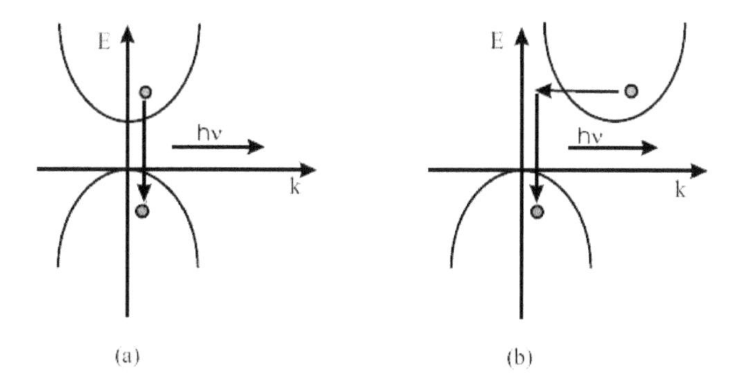

The difference lies in the fact that, in the first case, the minimum of the conduction band coincides with the maximum of the valence band and the electron-hole recombination can take place without involving the crystalline structure of the semiconductor.
In the second case, however, to maintain the conservation of momentum, the crystal will resonate at a certain frequency, a phenomenon which can be associated with the emission of a particle called a phonon.
All of this is detailed very well in the Physics of Matter, Solid State Physics, and Semiconductor Physics courses, and for that reason, we won't go back to it.

V – Lasers

Optical resonator

In a semiconductor laser, an optical resonator is composed of a series of layers of reflective material, sometimes coinciding with one side of the semiconductor itself, with reflectivity equal to:

$$R = \left(\frac{n-1}{n+1}\right)^2.$$

There may be various types of resonator: with parallel mirrors, confocal, hemispherical and in general, geometric optics is applied.
Said alpha the electron absorption coefficient, L the length of the resonator and defined the two radii of curvature of the mirrors placed at the resonator limits, there will be amplification of the light only above a gain (called threshold) equal to:

$$g_{th} = \alpha + \frac{1}{2L} ln\left(\frac{1}{R_1 R_2}\right)$$

In reality, not all the electromagnetic wave participates in amplification as part is transmitted at the output and part does not come into play in the active material.
The previous relation is corrected with a gamma factor less than one:

$$\Gamma g_{th} = \alpha + \frac{1}{2L} ln\left(\frac{1}{R_1 R_2}\right).$$

The Fabry-Perot condition imposes a relation on the length of the resonator for the establishment of standing waves:

$$L = m\frac{\lambda}{2n},$$

Where m is an integer.
Now, in a parallelepiped-shaped metal resonant cavity (of dimensions 2a, 2a, L), the oscillation frequencies of the modes of these standing waves are as follows:

$$\nu_{ilm} = \frac{c}{2}\sqrt{\left(\frac{i}{2a}\right)^2 + \left(\frac{l}{2a}\right)^2 + \left(\frac{m}{L}\right)^2}.$$

And the number of modes is given by:

$$N(\nu) = \frac{8\pi\nu^2}{c^3}\frac{V}{\Delta\nu_0} = 8\pi\frac{V}{\lambda^3}\frac{\Delta\lambda_0}{\lambda}$$

Where the width of the laser line is as follows:

$$\Delta\lambda_0 = \lambda^2 \Delta\nu_0 / c$$

In a dielectric cavity, the mode frequencies are:

$$\nu_{ilm} = \frac{c}{2}\sqrt{\left(\frac{m}{L}\right)^2 \left(1 + \frac{L^2}{m^2}\frac{i^2 + l^2}{(2a)^2}\right)} = \frac{c}{2}\left(\frac{m}{L} + \frac{1}{2}\frac{(i^2 + l^2)}{m}\frac{L}{4a^2}\right).$$

And the frequency difference between two longitudinal modes is given by:

$$\Delta\nu_m = \frac{c}{2L}.$$

While the frequency difference between two transverse modes is:

$$\Delta\nu_{i,l} = \frac{cL}{8ma^2}\left(l + \frac{1}{2}\right)$$

Semiconductor lasers

A semiconductor laser can exploit both the direct gap mechanism and the indirect gap mechanism.
In general, there is a tendency to divide these lasers according to the emission wavelength, the material used and the type of junction.
We speak of homojunction when we have a simple pn junction, of heterojunction when we have pnp (or npn), of double heterojunction when this mechanism is iterated twice.
We also speak of quantum hole lasers when the zone of different doping reaches atomic dimensions and of multiple quantum hole lasers when this mechanism is iterated for a number of times.
Based on the field confinement, a laser is said to be transversely or laterally guided.
Furthermore, based on the characteristics of the active medium, it is possible to have a gain guide or one linked to the refractive index.
There are semiconductor lasers that follow the Bragg condition and are called distributed Bragg reflectors.
Finally, there are vertical-cavity and surface-emitting lasers.

Lightning Source UK Ltd.
Milton Keynes UK
UKHW020751301222
414627UK00014B/837